For our first grandchild P.K.
For Jon S.P.

Text copyright © 1998 Pennie Kidd
Illustrations copyright © 1998 Susie Poole
This edition copyright © 1998 Lion Publishing

The moral rights of the author and illustrator
have been asserted

Published by
Lion Publishing plc
Sandy Lane West, Oxford, England
www.lion-publishing.co.uk
ISBN 0 7459 3764 0 (hardback)
ISBN 0 7459 4065 X (paperback)

First hardback edition 1998
10 9 8 7 6 5 4 3 2 1
First paperback edition 1999
10 9 8 7 6 5 4 3 2 1

A catalogue record for this book is available
from the British Library

Typeset in 22/42 Garamond ITC
Printed and bound in Singapore

Sleepy Jesus

Pennie Kidd

Illustrations by Susie Poole

LION
Children's Books

It was Christmas Eve.

God was very busy.

He mixed the colours for the

sunset and shaded the sun.

He drew the cloud curtains

together and pulled down the

heavy night sky.

God put the twinkle in the stars, pushed up the moon and sprinkled frost everywhere.

He had to work quickly.

There was no time to lose.

Tonight was very special. Baby Jesus would be born in a stable in Bethlehem, for there was no room at the inn.

Mary and Joseph were staying in the stable in Bethlehem. They had come a long way. They were tired and needed to rest.

Soon Baby Jesus was born on the hay. He was very small. Mary wrapped him in a cloth and sang to him. He slept quietly and Mary called him 'Sleepy Jesus'.

While Jesus slept the birds hushed their cooing. The dogs stopped barking. The donkey stopped braying. Even the cats stopped miaowing for sleepy Jesus. Only the mice whispered in the hay.

God hung a big, bright star in the east. He hushed the blowy wind. Everything was very still and quiet.

Wise men saw the star and travelled from far away. They had presents for Baby Jesus. They knew Jesus was special.

It wasn't quiet everywhere.
High in the sky near Bethlehem
choirs of angels sang with joy
about Baby Jesus.

Shepherds heard the angels singing in the sky. The angels told them to go to see Baby Jesus.

God pushed away the heavy night sky, dimmed the twinkling stars and opened the cloud curtains. He mixed the colours for the dawn, poured the paints across the sky and made the sun shine.

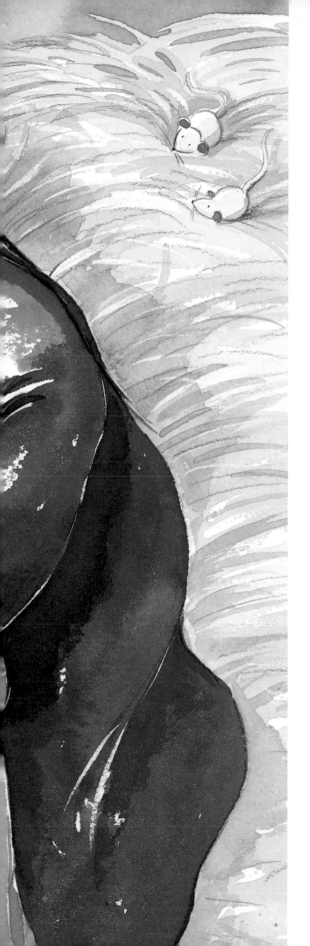

Jesus stirred. He rubbed his sleepy eyes; then he opened them. He smiled. God's love shone out from Baby Jesus. God smiled. It had been a busy night!

More paperbacks for young children from Lion Children's Books

Deedee's Easter Surprise   *Kay Kinnear and Julie Park*

God's Quiet Things   *Nancy Sweetland and Rick Stevens*

Henry's Song   *Kathryn Cave and Sue Hendra*

In the Beginning   *Steve Turner and Jill Newton*

The First Rainbow   *Su Box and Susie Poole*

When the World Was New   *Alicia Garcia de Lynam*

You Are Very Special   *Su Box and Susie Poole*